English edition first published in 2010 by Gecko Press
PO Box 9335, Marion Square, Wellington 6141, New Zealand
info@geckopress.com

© Gecko Press 2010

Original title: Meehr!!
© Carl Hanser Verlag München 2010

A catalogue record for this book is available from
the National Library of New Zealand.

Design by Luke Kelly, Wellington, New Zealand
Printed by Everbest, China

ISBN hardback 978-1-877467-55-4

For more curiously good books, visit www.geckopress.com

PETER SCHÖSSOW

MORE!

GECKO PRESS

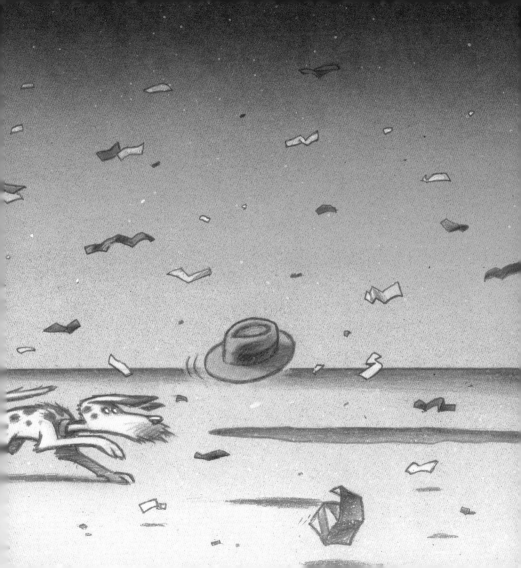

Peter Schössow was born in Germany in 1953.
He studied at the College of Design in Hamburg,
and has worked as an illustrator of books,
newspapers and magazines. He has written and
illustrated a large number of children's books for
which he has received numerous awards.